page 5

page 9

time	time	time	place
place	person	person	event

page 12

sion	sion	tion	tion
sion	sion	tion	tion
sion		tion	

page 14

page 20

eyes	dog	many	diary
children	phone	a	two
his	people	that	the

Leap Ahead Workbook
English
Home learning made fun

VOWELS

CONSONANTS

igloobooks

Speaking clearly

Decide which child is speaking correctly using standard English and cross out the incorrect speech bubbles. Remember, verbs like *seen* and *done* usually follow the verb *have*. For example, *he has seen* or *they have done*.

a
I seen an orange balloon in the sky.

b
I saw an orange balloon in the sky.

c
My friend Sam done a bike race last week.

d
My friend Sam did a bike race last week.

e
We was so busy, we didn't realise the time!

f
We were so busy, we didn't realise the time!

g
I love those sweets. They are my favourite.

h
I love them sweets. They are my favourite.

Answers on page 32

Past tense

Choose the correct verb forms to make the recount make sense.

Past progressive	Past simple	Present perfect
were hopping	ran	had walked
was running	were	have jumped
were trying	was	has jumped
were running	run	
was hopping	had	
	jumped	

Fun at trampoline world!

At the weekend, Charlie and Archie went to the brand new Trampoline World. They .... so excited to visit because Charlie's cousin said it had 27 trampolines! They .... up and down with excitement as they entered the building. Archie didn't realise he .... into the exit door and couldn't get in! After collecting new lime green socks at the counter, the boys .... quickly through the corridor to start their bounce session.

Charlie shouted, "I .... over two trampolines, come and watch me!"

Soon, the boys .... all sorts of stunts and jumps. They .... a great time.

Answers on page 32

PARENT TIP: Past progressive tense uses the verb *to be* plus the *ing* form of the second verb in the chain (e.g. *he was jumping* or *they were jumping*). Write out some sentences for your child with a space for them to write *was* or *were* (e.g. *she _____ walking / the two boys _____ reading / the old lady _____ shopping / the children _____ writing*).

Plural or possessive?

"Plural" means "more than one". When we make a noun plural, we usually add an *s* to the word. For example: *one cat* changes to *two cats*.

We also add an *s* at the end of a word when something belongs to someone. With these, we also use an apostrophe. For example, *Jenny's coat*, *the dog's tail*.

Can you work out when to use plurals or possessives? Tick the boxes next to the correct words.

The lady is looking after the ☐ baby's.
☐ babies.

Yesterday, ☐ Tom's
☐ Toms school shoes went missing.

Can you collect the ☐ books
☐ book's in please?

The ☐ trousers
☐ trouser's were too long.

The ☐ spots
☐ spot's were all over the ☐ leopards
☐ leopard's legs.

Answers on page 32

Vowels and consonants

The hungry shark only eats vowels! Draw a line from jellyfish to jellyfish to lead the shark to his cave, eating 12 vowels along the way. Remember to avoid any consonants. Vowels are *a e i o u*. Consonants are the rest of the letters in the alphabet (*b c d f g h j k l m n p q r s t v w x y z*).

Answers on page 32

Find a sticker to match each word. Draw a circle around the vowels in each word. Which word has the most vowels? Put a tick next to it.

place sticker here	bike	place sticker here	potatoes
place sticker here	circle	place sticker here	fruit
place sticker here	heart	place sticker here	island

5

Expanded noun phrases

Expanded noun phrases give clear descriptions using adjectives and preposition phrases. Design and draw your own superhero in the box below, then label the features using expanded noun phrases. For example, *lightweight, black cape on his back*. When you design your superhero, think about their clothes and special powers.

Create a character card with a picture and description. Use expanded noun phrases to describe your superhero. Then add rankings by writing what your superhero does (e.g. *flying* or *running*) and colouring in the stars depending on how good your superhero is at each thing.

SUPERHERO:

DESCRIPTION:

....

....

....

RANKING:

....

....

....

....

....

....

....

Fronted adverbials

Fronted adverbials tell you the time, place or manner of what is happening in a sentence. They are used to link one sentence to another. Underline all the fronted adverbials in the text about an ice cream shop below. Then sort them into the table under the correct heading. Two have been done for you.

Every day, the ice cream shop opens for business. On the promenade, it stands out from all the other shops because of its large ice cream sign.

Inside the shop, an array of colours hits you and attacks your senses. Carefully, the ice cream seller sets out each flavour in a rainbow assortment. A row of forty flavours stretches from one end of the shop to the other. In the long freezers, the flavours range from toffee to bubblegum. After lunch, a queue forms at the door of excited children and adults waiting to choose their flavour. Noisily, the children shuffle forward to select an ice cream. Which one to choose?

Time	Place	Manner
After lunch		Noisily

Can you add any more fronted adverbials of your own to the table?

Answers on page 32

Starting a paragraph

New paragraphs often start with a fronted adverbial to introduce a new time, place, person or event.

Match the stickers on the sticker sheet to the correct sentences to show whether the fronted adverbial is introducing a time, place, person or event.

place sticker here — Last night, there was a terrible storm.

place sticker here — Over the hill, a rainbow appeared.

place sticker here — In the hutch, the guinea pig snuggled up.

place sticker here — Cautiously, the girl crept down the alley.

place sticker here — Crash! Thunderously, the bridge collapsed at the start of the earthquake.

place sticker here — Silently, the dark, cloaked figure crept across the hall.

place sticker here — Suddenly, the teacher appeared from outside the classroom.

place sticker here — After several minutes, the train left from platform 4b.

Answers on page 32

Castle poems

Read the poem about the medieval forest and underline any fronted adverbials. Practise saying the poem aloud. Can you rehearse it and perform it out loud to your family or friends?

The Medieval Forest

Across the meadow, the tall trees towered.

Next to each other, standing like a regiment of soldiers.

In the undergrowth, the animals scurried.

Around them, crinkling, crunching noises sounded.

Beside the evergreen forest stood a castle.

Up above, its turrets ascended.

The castle, their protector.

Look at this zoomed-in picture of the castle. Can you see its turrets, drawbridge, arrow slits and portcullis? Create your own poem to describe the castle. Describe where the features are using fronted adverbials.

The Castle

Ending in *sion* or *tion*?

Read the story and look out for the scrambled up words causing confusion. Rearrange the letters to make words ending in either *sion* or *tion*, and write the correct word above each anagram.

Deep in the castle, the king had a sniiov.

He pictured an army attacking the castle and

causing fcosinnou. Before meeting his soldiers, the

king made a esdnicoi. They would not sit back and

wait for the soivnain. In ratpreniopa for the attack, he made a plan

of noicat. He decided it was time to tell his men. When he reached

the top of the castle to meet the soldiers, an awful sight met him —

his soldiers were suffering from a serious nnctiofei!

Add the sticker *sion* or *tion* from the sticker sheet at the end of each group of letters to spell the words correctly.

inva   *place sticker here*   prepara   *place sticker here*

confu   *place sticker here*   deci   *place sticker here*

infec   *place sticker here*   collec   *place sticker here*

vi   *place sticker here*   cau   *place sticker here*

ac   *place sticker here*   preci   *place sticker here*

Answers on page 32

Super sentences

Some sentences have two clauses: a main clause and a subordinate clause (which starts with a subordinating conjunction). You can swap the main clause and subordinate clause around.

The players wear their stripy kit when they play at home.

can be changed to

When they play at home, the players wear their stripy kit.

Rewrite the sentences below, swapping the clauses around. Remember to change where the capital letter and full stop are.

The starting whistle blew when the players were ready.

....

....

Everyone slipped around because it was so muddy.

....

....

The crowd cheered loudly if their team scored.

....

....

Now create a sentence of your own. Choose from these conjunctions: that, although, as, while, because, if, when, before, after.

....

Answers on page 32

Apostrophes

Match up the stickers on the sticker sheet with the correct sentences, then put the apostrophe in the correct place to make a possessive word. The first apostrophe has been done for you.

place sticker here	The baby's toys.
place sticker here	The footballers boots.
place sticker here	The knights helmet.
place sticker here	The firefighters hose.
place sticker here	The teachers books.

Answers on page 32

PARENT TIP: When the plural ends in s, the apostrophe comes after the s, e.g. *the boys' cloakroom*. If the word is an irregular plural without s at the end, the apostrophe comes before the s, e.g. *the children's books*.

Spelling word search

It is easy to confuse words that end with the suffix *ture* or *sure*. Can you find the words in the box in this word search? Put a tick next to each one once you've found it.

t	c	g	v	u	r	k	h	p	r	n	p
r	b	l	q	n	h	c	k	l	o	c	m
e	j	f	t	a	y	g	m	e	z	j	e
a	q	o	f	t	b	z	x	a	a	c	a
s	u	z	a	u	d	v	u	s	j	r	s
u	x	f	u	r	n	i	t	u	r	e	u
r	e	k	v	e	h	c	l	r	k	a	r
e	n	c	l	o	s	u	r	e	b	t	e
g	x	a	d	p	j	y	q	v	g	u	b
b	m	f	p	i	c	t	u	r	e	r	a
i	k	a	d	v	e	n	t	u	r	e	h

treasure	enclosure	pleasure
furniture	creature	adventure
measure	nature	picture

Answers on page 32

Nouns and pronouns

Look at these children having a great time on the high ropes. Write six sentences about what the children are doing using different nouns and pronouns to talk about them (e.g. *the children, they, the kids, the group*). The first sentence has been written for you.

Top tip!
When writing, try not to repeat the same noun or pronoun. It makes it boring for the reader.

The kids are running along the rickety wooden bridge.

You're becoming a fronted adverbial expert!

Look at this example sentence:
On top of the high rope, the children balanced carefully.

Add commas after fronted adverbials in these sentences:

From high in the sky the sun beamed down.

Cautiously the cat crept along the wall.

After lunch the children went out to play.

At sunset many swallows flew across the sky.

In the front room the children played their computer game.

Write a paragraph to describe a visit to an outdoor safari park.
Use fronted adverbials, commas and different nouns and pronouns.

....

....

....

....

....

....

....

....

....

....

Answers on page 32

Analysing text

Read the following story about a sleepover, then answer the questions about it on the next page.

The night had finally arrived! It was time for the sleepover. Lyra and Millie were very excited. Just after 5:00pm, they both arrived at Ruby's house and immediately changed into their pyjamas.

"Let's make cookies!" shouted Ruby. The three of them galloped down to the kitchen and rushed in to get ready to bake with big grins on their faces.

After an hour, a delicious smell was coming from the oven. They were busy playing party games and hadn't realised the cookies were ready until Ruby's dad called them. Huddling together on the bench, the friends ate one too many cookies and had to rub their tummies!

Bang! Pop! Guess what their next activity was? Balloon races! Everyone in the house was laughing and giggling… Everyone except Ruby's little cat, Fluff, who was cowering in the corner of the hall with her paws over her ears.

When it was time to settle down, ready for sleep, Lyra suggested they watch a film. The three buddies snuggled up together under a blanket and started watching the film trailers.

Suddenly, a loud click was heard and the house plunged into darkness. The only sound they could hear was Fluff meowing. "Oh no!" cried Ruby. "Not a power cut!"

1 How many children were at the sleepover?

....

2 How did the girls feel about baking?

....

....

3 Why did the girls rub their tummies?

....

....

4 Did Fluff enjoy the balloon games? How do you know?

....

....

5 Find and copy a word that suggests the children sat closely together.

....

6 How do you think the children felt after the power cut?

....

....

....

7 What do you think happened next?

....

....

....

Answers on page 32

Determiners

A determiner is a word used before a noun to explain exactly what the noun is referring to. Common determiners are *the, a, these* and *many*. Choose an appropriate determiner sticker and noun sticker from the sticker sheet to match the picture.

(a) (place sticker here) (place sticker here)

(b) (place sticker here) (place sticker here)

(c) (place sticker here) (place sticker here)

(d) (place sticker here) (place sticker here)

(e) (place sticker here) (place sticker here)

(f) (place sticker here) (place sticker here)

Write a sentence using determiners and nouns.

....

....

....

....

Answers on page 32

Curious spellings

Complete the crossword with words that end in *ous* using the clues in the box below. Some letters have already been added to help you.

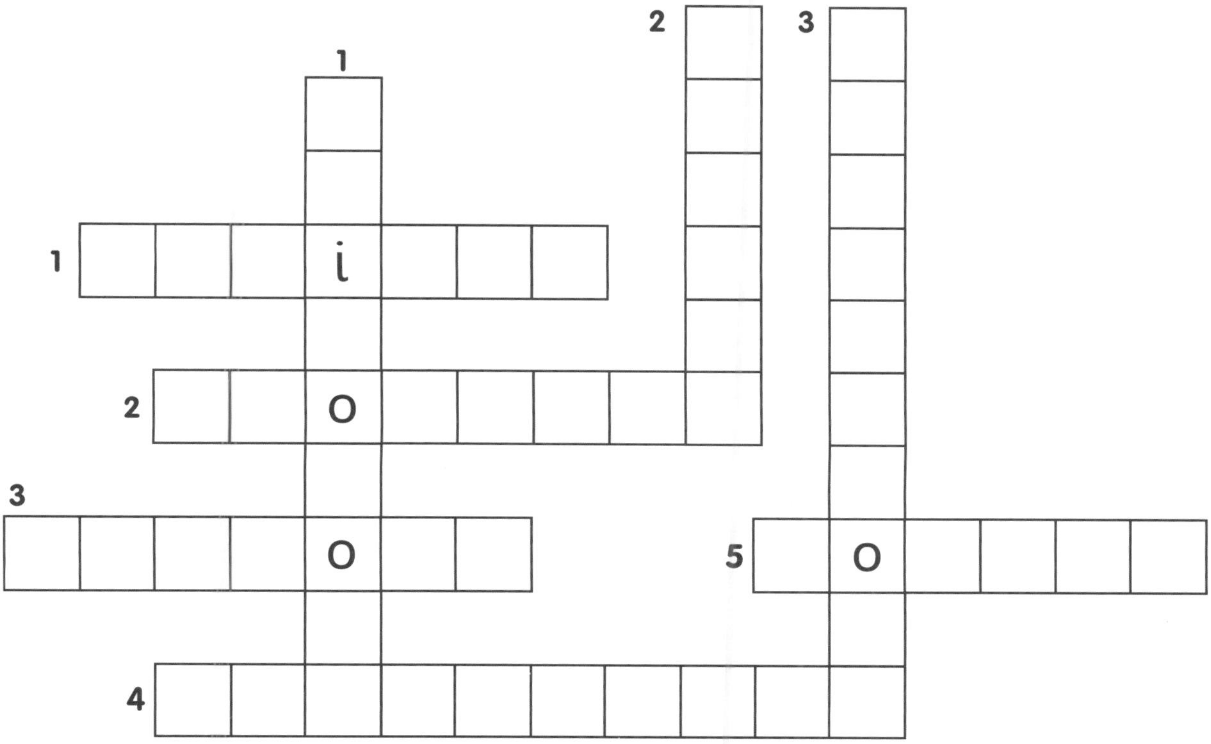

(Crossword grid with pre-filled letters: Across 1 contains "i", Across 2 contains "o", Across 3 contains "o", Across 5 begins with "o")

ACROSS
1 - A person who asks questions
2 - An elephant compared to a mouse is...
3 - Another word for 'many'
4 - When something bad happens, it is...
5 - A happy person is often...

DOWN
1 - A snake with venom is...
2 - A well-known celebrity is...
3 - Someone who is very brave

Answers on page 32

What do you notice about the spellings?

....

Can you find a rule?

....

21

Using direct speech

Read through the following conversations.

a

I've lost my dog! Can you help?

When did you last see it?

b

Please can I have some sweets? I have 50p.

Yes. I'll do you a mixed bag.

c

Look out! There's a rock on the road there.

Don't worry. I've seen it! I'll skate around it.

Top tip: there are five rules for writing direct speech correctly.

1. You need a comma after a reporting clause.
2. Spoken words are written inside a pair of inverted commas: "___".
3. A capital letter should be used at the start of speech.
4. Use a comma inside the inverted commas if your sentence carries on after the speech has finished.
5. Each new speaker needs a new line.

Now write the speech from the speech bubbles into direct speech below. Remember to use the five rules to write direct speech correctly. The first one has been done for you.

a) "I've lost my dog! Can you help?" asked the girl

b)

c)

Adverb exceptions

You can create adverbs from adjectives by adding the suffix *ly*.
Sometimes, you have to modify the word using these rules:

1. If the word ends in *y*, change it to *i* (e.g. *snappy* / *snappily*).
2. Following *ic* add *ally* (e.g. *frantic* / *frantically*).
3. If a word ends in *le*, change the *e* to a *y* (e.g. *wiggle* / *wiggly*)
4. Just add *ly* to all the others.

Change the words below into adverbs using the rules.

(a) frantic ....

(b) happy ....

(c) gentle ....

(d) kind ....

(e) angry ....

(f) basic ....

(g) prickle ....

(h) merry ....

(i) classic ....

(j) cautious ....

(k) crazy ....

Choose an adverb from the list above and write a sentence using it.

....

....

....

Answers on page 32

Expanded noun phrases

Draw a new pet in the box below. It can be an imaginary pet or one made from the features of other pets. Think about its head, body, arms and legs, and if it has any other features such as claws, a tail or a beak.

Write expanded noun phrases to describe your pet. Make it sound like a great pet to have.

....

....

....

....

....

....

Persuasive writing

Imagine your pet is for sale in a pet shop. Design a poster to advertise your pet. Remember all the features of persuasive writing:

1. emotive language (e.g. you will never have a more loving pet)
2. clear descriptions using expanded noun phrases
3. questions
4. adverbs.

Your poster should have: a picture, the name and price of the pet, a detailed description about it and a paragraph about why someone should buy it.

Write a letter to your friend telling them all about the new pet, and persuade them to buy it. Use the persuasive writing features (listed on page 26) to make sure your letter contains the right details.

Proofreading

Read this recount about a trip to the museum. Proofread the writing to check if there are any spelling or punctuation mistakes. Change the mistakes with a coloured pen.

While proofreading, you should check for: capital letters and full stops, questions and exclamation marks, apostrophes for possession, commas after fronted adverbials, speech punctuation and spelling.

On thursday 1st March, Class 4 visited a museum, which was an hour away from their school

Once the teacher had taken the register the class lined up in pears to get on the coach. excited children chated all the way to the museum.

When they arrived, the teacher led them into the entrance hall and counted to check everywon was their. "Come on! he shouted. "We're off to the Ancient Greeks sechion!"

Wandering threw the museum, the children spotted vases and bowls like they had seen in class.

when it was time to leave, they had to collect the childrens coats from the cloakroom. What a fantastic trip it had been

Answers on page 32

Spelling practice

Can you spell all of these words? You have practised all the rules for them in this book. Ask an adult to test you or write out your spellings then check them yourself.

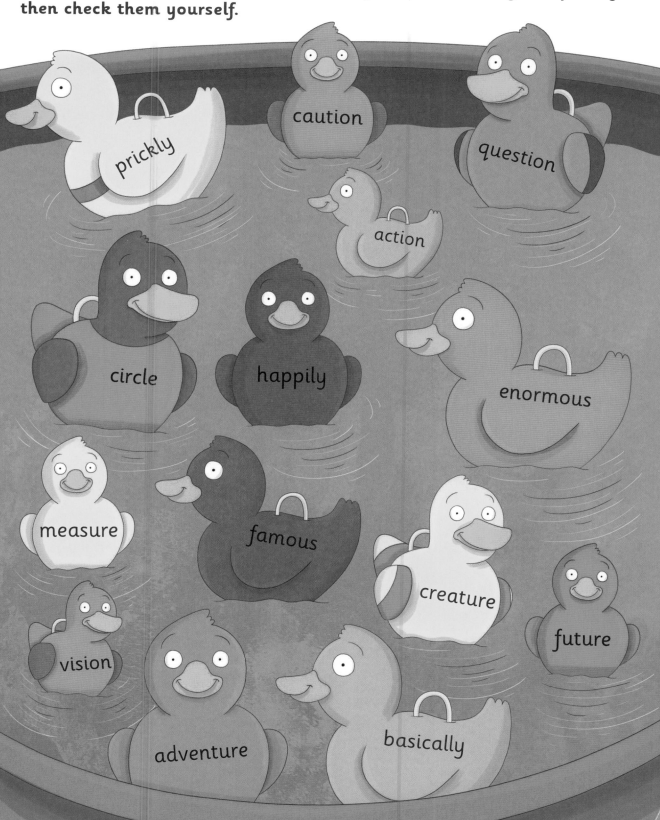

prickly

caution

question

action

circle

happily

enormous

measure

famous

creature

future

vision

adventure

basically

Writing a recount

Use this page to plan a recount about the best day of your life.

Note down some ideas for each section using the bullet points.

Introduction (tell the reader about yourself using the present tense):

- ....
- ....
- ....
- ....

Best time in your life (describe people and places using the past tense):

- ....
- ....
- ....
- ....

Challenging time in your life (describe people/places using the past tense):

- ....
- ....
- ....
- ....

Summary (write about your hopes for the future using the future tense):

- ....
- ....
- ....
- ....

Write a blog post about the best day of your life in four paragraphs, following the plan you've created. Remember to use: fronted adverbials, direct speech for quotes, expanded noun phrases for description and correct punctuation.

Answers

Page 2: Speaking clearly
The correct sentences are: b, d, f, g

Page 3: Past tense
were/were hopping/had walked/ran/jumped/were trying/had

Page 4: Plural or possessive?
babies / Tom's / books / trousers / spots / leopard's

Page 5: Vowels and consonants

bike   circle   heart   potatoes   fruit   island

Page 8: Fronted adverbials

Time	Place	Manner
After lunch Every day	Inside the shop On the promenade In the long freezers	Noisily Carefully

Page 9: Starting a paragraph
Time: Last night, there was a terrible storm.
After several minutes, the train left from platform 4b.
Suddenly, the teacher appeared from outside the classroom.
Place: In the hutch, the guinea pig snuggled up.
Over the hill, a rainbow appeared.
Person: Cautiously, the girl crept down the alley.
Silently, the dark, cloaked figure crept across the hall.
Event: Crash! Thunderously, the bridge collapsed at the start of the attack.

Page 12: Ending in *sion* or *tion*?
vision / confusion / decision / invasion / preparation / action / infection
Endings: invasion, confusion, infection, vision, action, preparation, decision, collection, caution, precision

Page 13: Super sentences
When the players were ready, the starting whistle blew.
Because it was so muddy, everyone slipped around.
If their team scored, the crowd cheered loudly.

Page 14: Apostrophes
baby's toys / footballers' boots / knight's helmet / firefighters' hose / teachers' books

Page 15: Spelling word search

t	c	g	v	u	r	k	h	p	r	n	p
r	b	l	q	n	h	c	k	l	o	c	m
e	j	f	t	a	y	g	m	e	z	j	e
a	q	o	f	t	b	z	x	a	a	c	a
s	u	z	a	u	d	v	u	s	j	r	s
u	x	f	u	r	n	i	t	u	r	e	u
r	e	k	v	e	h	c	l	r	k	a	r
e	n	c	l	o	s	u	r	e	b	t	e
g	x	a	d	p	j	y	q	v	g	u	b
b	m	f	p	i	c	t	u	r	e	r	a
i	k	a	d	v	e	n	t	u	r	e	h

Page 17: Nouns and pronouns
From high in the sky, the sun beamed down.
Cautiously, the cat crept along the wall.
After lunch, the children went out to play.
At sunset, many swallows flew across the sky.
In the front room, the children played their computer game.

Page 19: Analysing text
1. Three. 2. Excited/happy. 3. They had eaten too many cookies. 4. No, Fluff was scared. We know this because she was hiding in the corner of the hall with her paws covering her ears. 5. snuggled 6. scared, nervous, worried 7. (no single correct answer for this question.)

Page 20: Determiners
Various possible answers, e.g. a) The children b) That dog
c) Two eyes d) His diary e) A phone f) Many people

Page 21: Curious spellings
1 across: curious   4 across: disastrous   2 down: famous
2 across: enormous   5 across: joyous   3 down: courageous
3 across: various   1 down: poisonous

Pages 22–23: Using direct speech
a) "I've lost my dog! Can you help?" asked the girl.
"When did you last see it?" replied the police officer.
b) "Please can I have some sweets? I have 50p," explained the boy.
"Yes. I'll do you a mixed bag," said the shopkeeper.
c) "Look out! There's a rock on the road there," shouted the skater to his friend.
"Don't worry. I've seen it! I'll skate around it," the other skater shouted back.

Page 24: Adverb exceptions
a) frantically b) happily c) gently d) kindly e) angrily f) basically
g) prickly h) merrily i) classically j) cautiously k) crazily

Page 28: Proofreading
On **T**hursday 1st March, Class 4 visited a museum, which was an hour away from their school**.** Once the teacher had taken the register**,** the class lined up in **pairs** to get on the coach. **E**xcited children chat**t**ed all the way to the museum. When they arrived, the teacher led them into the entrance hall and counted to check every**one** was the**re**. "Come on**!**" he shouted. "We're off to the Ancient Greeks sec**t**ion!" Wandering **through** the museum, the children spotted vases and bowls like they had seen in class. **W**hen it was time to leave, they had to collect the children**'**s coats from the cloakroom. What a fantastic trip it had been**.**